THE ENGLISH RUNES
STUDY JOURNAL

Suzanne Rance

Dragon House

First Printed 2017

Published by
Dragon House

suzanne@suzannerance.co.uk
www.suzannerance.co.uk

ISBN 978 0 9957264 1 3

How to use this study journal

This study journal is designed as a companion to The English Runes *Secrets of Magic, Spells and Divination.*

It has been created to aid you in your personal journey as you learn about the English Runes, and runic magic. Here you can record your thoughts and experiences; however disconnected these may seem as you write them down, revisiting your work will deepen your knowledge and understanding.

My hope is that this journal will become an invaluable resource, and that through your own thoughts and explorations you will become an expert practitioner.

Remember it is your own personal connection to each individual rune and the magic that surrounds it that brings the runes to life and makes them sing.

Suzanne Rance
Sussex, England
Spring 2017

Contents

How to use this study journal 1

Feoh – Wealth 5

Ūr – Aurochs 9

Þorn – Thorn 13

Ōs – God..17

Rād – Riding 21

Cēn – Torch 25

Gyfu – Gift 29

Wen - Happiness 33

Hægl – Hail 37

Nyd – Need..41

Īs – Ice 45

Gēr – Harvest...49

Ēoh – Yew 53

Peorð – Gaming 57

Eolhx – Elk 61

Sigel – Sun 65

Tīr – Tiw (a god) 69

Beorc – Birch 73

Eh – Horse..77

Man – Mankind 81

Lagu – Water (Large body of) 85

Ing – Ing (a god, thought to be Frea) 89

Ēðel – Homeland 93

Dæg – Day 97

Āc – Oak 101

Æsc – Ash 105

Yr – Bow of yew 109

Īar – Beaver 113

Ēar – Grave, one of the sea or the earth 117

Notes on Wyrd 121

General Notes 125

Feoh - Wealth

Wealth is a comfort to any man
yet each person must share it out well
if he wants to win a good name before his lord.
Pollington

Ūr - Aurochs

Aurochs is fierce and high-horned
the courageous beast fights with it's horns
a well-known moor-treader, it is a brave
creature.
Pollington

Þorn - Thorn

Thorn is painfully sharp to any warrior
seizing it is bad, excessively severe
for any person who lays among them.
Pollington

Ōs - God

God is the origin of all language
wisdom's foundation and wise man's comfort
and to every hero blessing and hope.

Pollington

Rād - Riding

Riding is for every man in the hall
easy, and strenuous for him who sits upon
a powerful horse along the long paths.
Pollington

Cēn - Torch

*Torch is known to each living being by fire
radiant and bright, it usually burns
where nobles rest indoors.*
Pollington

Gyfu - Gift

Gift is an honour and grace of men
a support and adornment, and for any exile
mercy and sustenance when he has no other.
Pollington

Wen - Happiness

Happiness he cannot enjoy who knows little woe
pain and sorrow, and has for himself
wealth and joy, and sufficient protection too.
Pollington

Hægl - Hail

Hail is whitest of corn, from heaven's height
it whirls, winds blow it,
it becomes water after.
Pollington

Nyd - Need

*Need is hard on the heart, yet for men's
sons it often becomes
a help and healing if they heed it before.*
Pollington

Īs – Ice

I

Ice is too cold and extremely slippery
glass-clear it glistens most like gems
a floor made of frost, fair in appearance.
Pollington

Gēr - Harvest

Harvest is men's hope when god allows
-holy king of heaven – the earth to give up
fair fruits to warriors and to wretches.
Pollington

Ēoh - Yew

Yew is an unsmooth tree outside
hard, earthfast, fire's keeper,
underpinned with roots, a joy in the homeland.
Pollington

Peorð - Gaming

*Gaming is always play and laughter
to proud men... where warriors sit
in the beerhall happily together.*
Pollington

Eolhx - Elk

Elk-grass most often dwells in a fen,
grows in water, harshly wounds
marks with blood any warrior
who tries to take it.
Pollington

Sigel - Sun

Sun to seamen is always a hope
when they travel over the fish's bath
until the sea-steed brings them to land.
Pollington

Tīr - Tiw (a god)

Tiw is one of the signs, holds faith well
with noblemen, on a journey is always
Above the night's gloom, never fails.
Pollington

71

Beorc - Birch

Birch is fruitless, yet bears
shoots without seeds, is pretty in its branches
high in its spread, fair adorned
laden with leaves, touching the sky.
Pollington

Eh - Horse

Steed is noblemen's joy before heroes,
a hoof-proud horse where about it warriors
rich in stallions exchange words
and is always a comfort to the restless.
Pollington

Man - Mankind

Man is dear to his kinsmen in mirth
yet each one must fail the others
since by his judgement the lord wishes
to commit the poor flesh to earth.
Pollington

Lagu – Water (Large body of)

Water is seemingly endless to men
if they must fare on a tilting ship
and sea-waves frighten them mightily
and the sea-steed does not heed the bridle.
Pollington

Ing - Ing (a god, thought to be Frea)

Ing was first among the East Danes
seen by men until he later eastwards
went across the waves, the waggon sped behind,
Thus the hard men named the hero.
Pollington

Ēðel - Homeland

Homeland is very dear to every man
if there rightfully and with propriety he may
enjoy wealth in his dwelling generally.
Pollington

Dæg - Day

Day is the Lord's sending, dear to men,
god's splendid light, joy and hope
to the blessed and the wretched, a benefit to all.
Pollington

Āc - Oak

Oak is for the sons of men on earth
a feeder of flesh, often travels
over gannet's bath, the ocean tests
whether the oak keeps good faith.
Pollington

Æsc - Ash

Ash is very tall, dear to men,
strong in foundations, holds its place properly
though many men fight against it.
Pollington

Yr - Bow of yew

*Yew bow for every noble and warrior is
a joy and adornment, is fair on a steed
a trusty piece of wargear on a journey.*
Pollington

Īar - Beaver

Beaver is a riverfish yet it always enjoys food on land, has a fine dwelling surrounded by water where it lives happily.
Pollington

Ēar - Grave, one of the sea or the earth

Grave is frightful to every warrior
when the flesh begins inexorably
the corpse to cool, to embrace the earth
the dark as its companion; fruits fall away,
joys pass away, promises fail.

Pollington

Notes on Wyrd

General Notes